July /71

Happy birthday

To

From
...phanie

Happiness is Everywhere

Happiness is Everywhere

By Dean Walley

Illustrated by Alice Ann Biggerstaff

HALLMARK EDITIONS

Happiness is
Everywhere

Where does happiness come from?

What makes happiness start?

How does it come out of nowhere
And into a person's heart?

Sometimes it's part
Of a dream that comes true,

Or perhaps it's just doing
What we like to do.

Happiness comes from laughing--
Laughing together...

And from a bright change
In some unpleasant weather.

Happiness comes
From a prayer we've said

It's the feeling we get
When we're tucked into bed.

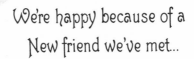

We're happy because of a
New friend we've met...

Or because of a gift
We had hoped we would get.

Sometimes happiness comes
Without any warning.

It may beam in our window
First thing in the morning.

Happiness comes
From a secret we shared,

Or from a special surprise
We prepared.

We often find happiness
In learning new things...

In a job we've done well
And the praise that it brings.

It is found in the wonder
Of blue sky above...

In the magic of being
With someone we love.

And when happiness seems
To be nowhere around,

Remember...it's waiting
Just to be found.

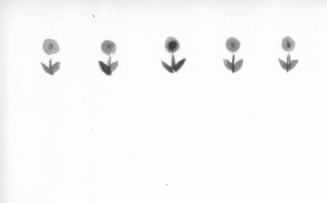